AN ENGLISH K

AN ENGLISH
KYRIALE

MUSIC FOR THE EUCHARIST

Edited by
Peter Allan C R, Mary Berry, David Hiley,
Pamela C S J B, Ernest Warrell

Community of the Resurrection
HarperCollins

First published in Great Britain in 1991
by
Community of the Resurrection
Mirfield, West Yorkshire WF14 0BN
and
HarperCollinsReligious
part of HarperCollins Publishers
77–85 Fulham Palace Road
London W6 8JB

A recording of the music in this book can be obtained from
Mirfield Publications, House of the Resurrection
Mirfield, West Yorkshire WF14 0BN

Calligraphy by Joy Dodson, Harpenden, Herts
Typeset in Poliphilus with Omnia display by The Stingray Office, Oxford
Printed and bound in Great Britain by HarperCollins Manufacturing, Glasgow

CONTENTS

ACKNOWLEDGMENTS

THe publication of this Kyriale has been made possible by the generous support and co-operation of many people. The editors are particularly grateful to the Plainsong and Mediaeval Music Society under whose auspices the project was begun. Thanks are due to the Society not only for the initial support, but also for relinquishing any rights in order that the work could be brought to publication in this present form. Much of the material is based on the musical texts edited by Professor Nick Sandon in *The Use of Salisbury*, Vol. I: *The Ordinary of the Mass* (Antico Church Music), and we are grateful for his co-operation. We are similarly grateful to the Abbot and monks of the Abbaye Saint-Pierre de Solesmes, on whose editions some of this work is founded. Joy Dodson, who prepared the manuscript for printing, also deserves a special word of thanks.

The texts of the 'Gloria in Excelsis', Creed, 'Sanctus', and 'Agnus' are copyright © the International Consultation on English Texts (I C E T), 1970, 1971, 1975. The revisions are copyright © the English Language Liturgical Consultation (E L L C), 1988.

INTRODUCTION

I. HISTORICAL NOTE

IN 1896 the Plainsong and Mediaeval Music Society first issued a col⁄
lection of chants entitled *The Ordinary of the Mass*. This collection, best
known in the revised edition of 1937, is still available. The music is chiefly
adapted from mediaeval books of the Use of Salisbury. These were ar⁄
ranged with considerable skill by H Briggs and W H Frere, C R, al⁄
though the work was published anonymously — to the words of the Book
of Common Prayer. A volume of organ accompaniments, now very rare,
was published in 1910; and two simple sets of chants were selected from
the collection and published in 1899 in small format in what became
affectionately known as 'The Little Red Book', also currently in print.

Although still used, these books are less suitable for present⁄day congre⁄
gations in view of recent liturgical revision. Need for new adaptations of
plainchant has been widely felt, because of the reforms within the Roman
Catholic Church after the Second Vatican Council and within the
Church of England. There are by now myriad versions of chants to the
new texts, some published, most in use only in the church or religious
community where they were put together. Some are systematic attempts to
provide for the yearly cycle of worship, some consist of but a single set of
melodies for the Eucharist. It is to meet the need, clearly evident from all
this activity, that the present collection of chants for the Ordinary has been
compiled. It began life as just such a 'private' collection as those alluded
to, arranged for the Anglican Community of St John Baptist at Windsor.
When interest was shown by the P M M S, Sister Pamela, C S J B, was
joined by the other members of the editorial team and her work taken as a
basis for further adaptation and enlargement.

The texts in this volume are those agreed by the International Consul⁄
tation on English Texts. These texts have now been revised by the English
Language Liturgical Consultation. The editors have not found it necessary
to make major changes. Any small adjustments made by E L L C can be
incorporated without difficulty, with the exception of the 'Et incarnatus' in

the Creed, which has been entirely recast. However, in the introduction to *Praying Together* we note the following: 'Some Churches may wish to sing the texts to traditional plainsong or Anglican Chant. This may necessitate some modification of the punctuation and adjustment of the lines. It may also be found advisable occasionally to insert a word or syllable to make a necessary change in the rhythm.' It is the fervent hope of the present editors that these chants will be sung in as many churches as possible, but especially in those where the new English texts have been adopted.

The editors have not felt it necessary to delve deeply into the great wealth of mediaeval melodies for the Ordinary which scholarship has brought to light. We have relied on the well-loved music present in the PMMS collection and in the Solesmes Kyriale, familiar above all from the *Liber Usualis* and the *Graduale Romanum*. When there was a choice of versions, we have usually (but not exclusively) followed the Salisbury musical readings, which often differ in some details from the versions in modern Vatican books. It has seemed to us valuable to preserve an 'English' character for the collection, a faint echo of the rich diversity of musical practice so typical of the mediaeval church. In pursuing Salisbury versions of the melodies, we have drawn upon the fine edition published by Professor Nick Sandon: *The Use of Salisbury: The Ordinary of the Mass* (Antico Church Music, Newton Abbott, 1984). The Solesmes versions have been adapted with permission from the *Graduale Romanum*, 1974 (Édition de Solesmes).

The principal model for each of the chants is set out in the table at the back of the book. The other commonly known versions of the melodies are cited in parentheses.

II. AIMS AND METHOD

IN making these new adaptations the editors have sought above all else to let the melodies speak for themselves. Whenever possible the complete line of a melody, with its verbal accents intact, has been presented unchanged. In general the English text has fewer syllables, and this has required a new grouping of the notes. In making such changes we have had before us the models of mediaeval arrangers, and we have conformed to their practice whenever a parallel was available.

Three distinct problems attracted our attention. First, the obvious need for care in setting unimportant syllables, eg 'the', 'of', 'a', '-ed', etc. Thus we have sometimes changed the distribution of notes to syllables, even where the number of syllables and the pattern of accentuation in English corresponds to the Latin, in order to avoid an ugly and unmusical result.

SANCTUS IV

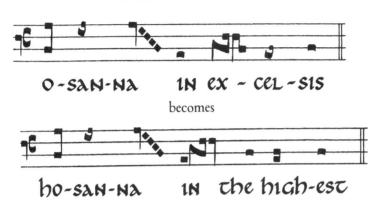

O -SAN-NA   IN EX ~ CEL-SIS

becomes

ho-SAN-NA   IN the high-est

Second, the brevity of the English text. The opening of the *Agnus Dei* (Lamb of God) illustrates a general characteristic and the principles of our approach.

AGNUS DEI II

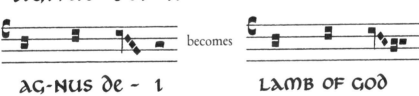

AG-NUS DE ~ I   LAMB OF GOD

Here the aim has been to retain the weight and balance of the Latin, unlike the 1937 edition:

O LAMB OF GOD

In this example, although the English has four syllables, the inversion of the accents results in an unhappy distortion of the original.

xi

The third problem is the most intractable. It occurs particularly in the *Gloria in excelsis* and wherever the new English text is not a translation of the original. The phrase 'and peace to his people on earth' is not a translation of the Latin 'et in terra pax hominibus bonae voluntatis', nor does it correspond in length or shape, having only eight syllables to the Latin's fifteen. All those familiar with the Latin originals will feel here a certain abruptness. There was no alternative but to recast the phrase. This we have done, with careful reference to the construction of phrases and cadence points in each piece. Further difficulties are caused by the inversion of parts of the text. In the English 'Lord God, heavenly King' ('Domine Deus, Rex caelestis') comes before 'We worship you,' etc. ('Laudamus te,...'). In general we have chosen to invert the melody also, when the construction of the piece and its cadential points allowed; for there is an element of sensitivity to the meaning of the words in the original that is not unimportant. In two cases we have preferred to follow the course of the music and to shape the text to it. The English text also has entire phrases missing or substantially re-arranged: the only satisfactory solution has been to omit phrases of the melody.

From the table that lists the principal models for each piece it will be seen that for Glorias VII and IX we have chosen the Vatican melodies because they are more sympathetic to the English words. It is interesting that Dr Palmer also followed the Vatican reading (although without acknowledgment) in the version of Gloria IX he supplied for the original published collection (P M M S VIII).

III. HOW TO SING THE CHANTS

IT is easier to sing chant from its traditional square notation than from a modern transcription, so we shall give here a brief summary of the principal note-forms used in this book and their meaning.

Staves and Clefs

A four-line staff is used for chant:

because the range of the melodies rarely exceeds an octave.

The *doh* clef on the top line:

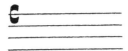

indicates the position of the major tonic, *doh*. To sing down from this line to the space immediately below gives the notes *doh–te*, a semitone, or half-step:

and one can continue down the major scale, from line to space, by tones and semitones (whole steps and half-steps), like this:

The *doh* clef sometimes appears one line further down, or even two lines further down:

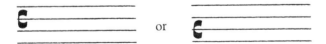

These positions of the *doh* clef are used when the melody rises more than one note above the *doh*, for example:

A *fah* clef is sometimes used, and it shows the position of the other semitone (half-step), *fah–me*. It is found with melodies that are sung in this lower part of the scale:

faḥ me ḋoḥ ṛay

Remember always to check which clef is used before beginning to sing!

Both the *doh* clef and the *fah* clef indicate relative, not absolute pitch. This means that you can choose a pitch for your *doh* or your *fah* that best suits your own singers.

Note Shapes

1. *Single notes*

The small black square ■ indicates a single note sung to a single syllable.

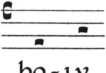

ḥo - ḻy

2. *Two notes to one syllable*

high–low

ḥo - ḻy

and

low–high

LAṂB OF GOḋ

3. *Three notes to one syllable*

low–high–low

aṇḋ peace

high–low–high

LAṂB OF GOḋ

xiv

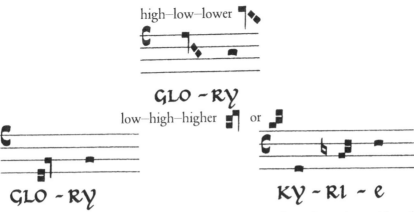

(NB: The flattened 7th degree of the major scale is the only accidental used in chant.)

4. More than three notes to one syllable

For longer runs the melody is simply built up by adding extra notes and combining the groups, for instance as follows:

5. Special forms: liquescent and quilisma

   (a) liquescent

high–low ⌐L sometimes appears like this: ♫

low–high ◼ sometimes appears like this: ♪

These are called *liquescent* forms and are used for singing through certain letters, 'l', 'm', or 'n', for example, gently, quietly, almost hummed:

ho-san-na

ho-san-na

Liquescence is sometimes used for the second note of a diphthong, or for an awkward combination of consonants.

(b) quilisma

low–high–higher ♫ sometimes appears like this: ♫

The little saw-edged note in the middle of the group is called a *quilisma*. It is interpreted as a light, short note, leading upwards to the note above. In practice the note or notes immediately preceding it are lengthened:

(approximately ♩ (♪) ♩ ♫ ♩ ♩)

Duration

Each individual note has roughly the duration of a single short syllable in ordinary speech. But there was probably never intended to be a rigidly fixed time-value in the chant. The natural rhythm of the text itself when read aloud in a normal speaking voice is probably the most reliable guide to a flexible and lively performance. However, in one or two places where a lengthening occurs in the original musical text, this is indicated by a short horizontal line over or under the affected note.

Phrasing

The musical text, like the verbal text, has its 'punctuation', shown by the following phrase divisions:

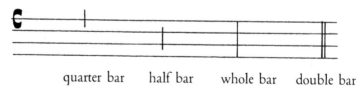

quarter bar   half bar   whole bar   double bar

The quarter bar ═══╪═══ corresponds roughly to the comma.

The half bar ═══╪═══ corresponds roughly to the colon.

The whole bar ═══╬═══ corresponds roughly to the full stop.

The double bar ═══╫═══ marks the end of a section, either the end of a paragraph or of a complete piece. It is also used between short phrases when these are sung in alternation, as in the *Gloria*, between the two halves of the choir or between a cantor and the choir.

Before each of these divisions there is a natural lengthening of the last syllable or syllables. Here too the natural phrasing of the verbal text is the best guide to the musical phrasing.

IT is our hope that those who sing these arrangements will find in them a rich vehicle for prayer, the very quality that has ensured their survival. Further, the experience of singing these pieces may be an incentive to discover more of the vast treasury of Western Chant.

Peter Allan, C R
Mary Berry
David Hiley
Pamela, C S J B
Ernest Warrell

KYRIE ELEISON

1

LUX ET ORIGO

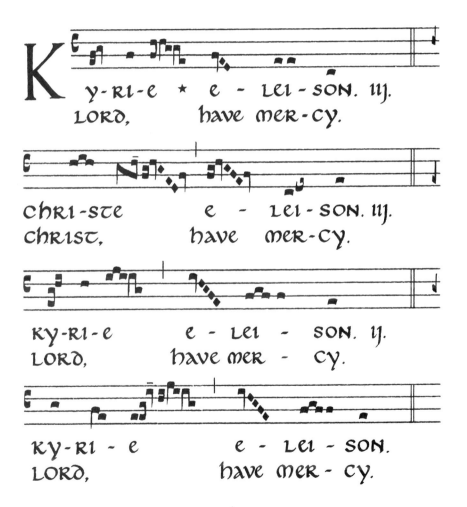

Ky-ri-e ★ e - lei - son. iij.
Lord, have mer-cy.

Chri-ste e - lei - son. iij.
Christ, have mer-cy.

Ky-ri-e e - lei - son. ij.
Lord, have mer - cy.

Ky-ri - e e - lei - son.
Lord, have mer - cy.

II
REX SPLENDENS

KY-RI - e *   e - LEI - SON. iij.
LORD,   have mer-cy.

CHRI-STE   e - LEI-SON.iij.
CHRIST,   have mer-cy.

KY-RI-e   e - LEI - SON.iij.
LORD,   have mer-cy.

III
CUNCTIPOTENS

KY-RI - e *   e - LEI-SON. iij.
LORD,   have mer-cy.

CHRI·STE   e - LEI SON. IIJ.
CHRIST,   have MER-cy.

KY·RI - e   e - LEI - SON.   IJ.
LORD,   have MER - cy.

KY·RI - e   e - LEI - SON.
LORD,   have MER - cy.

IV

ORBIS FACTOR

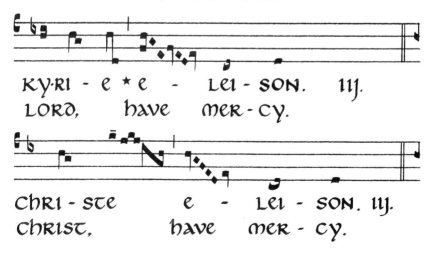

KY·RI - e ★ e - LEI - SON.   IIJ.
LORD,   have   MER - cy.

CHRI - STE   e - LEI - SON. IIJ.
CHRIST,   have   MER - cy.

KY-RI-e   e   -   LEI-SON.   ij.
LORD,   have   mer-cy.

KY - RI - e   e   -   LEI-SON.
LORD,   have   mer-cy.

v

KY-RI-e*e - LEI-SON. KY-RI-e   e - LEI-SON.
LORD, have mer-cy.   LORD,   have mer-cy.

KY-RI-e e - LEI-SON. CHRI-STE   e - LEI-SON.
LORD, have mer-cy.   CHRIST,   have mer-cy.

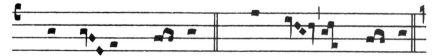

CHRI-STE   e - LEI-SON. CHRI-STE   e - LEI-SON.
CHRIST, have mer-cy.   CHRIST,   have mer-cy.

KY-RI-e e - LEI-SON. KY-RI-e e - LEI-SON.
LORD, have mer-cy. LORD, have mer-cy.

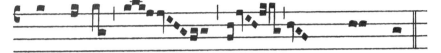

KY-RI-e   e - LEI-SON.
LORD,   have mer-cy.

VI

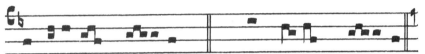

KY-RI-e*e - LEI-SON.iij. CHRI-STE e - LEI-SON.
LORD, have mer-cy.   CHRIST, have mer-cy.

KY-RI-e - LEI-SON. ij. KY-RI-e - LEI-SON.
LORD, have mer-cy.   LORD, have mer-cy.

VII

KY-RI-e * e - LEI-SON. KY-RI-e e - LEI-SON.
LORD, have mer-cy. LORD, have mer-cy.

5

KY-RI-e e - LEI-SON. CHRI-STE e - LEI-SON.
LORD, have mer-cy. CHRIST, have mer-cy.

CHRI-STE e - LEI-SON. CHRI-STE e - LEI-SON.
CHRIST, have mer-cy. CHRIST, have mer-cy.

KY-RI-e e - LEI-SON. KY-RI-e e - LEI-SON.
LORD, have mer-cy. LORD, have mer-cy.

KY-RI-e   e - LEI - SON.
LORD,   have mer - cy.

VIII

1.

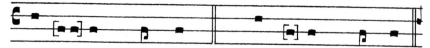

KY-RI-e*e - LEI-SON. iij. CHRI-STE e - LEI-SON. iij
LORD, have mer-cy.   CHRIST, have mer-cy.

1. In English omit these notes

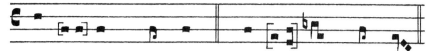

KY-RI-e e - LEI-SON. iJ. KY-RI-e e - LEI-SON.
LORD, have mer-cy.   LORD, have mer-cy.

IX

KY-RI-e   *   e - LE - I-SON. iiJ.
LORD,   have mer - cy.

CHRI-STE   e - LE - I-SON. iiJ.
CHRIST,   have mer- cy.

KY-RI-e   e - LE- I-SON. KY-RI-
LORD,   have mer-cy.   LORD,

~e   *   **   e - LE - I-SON.
                            have mer - cy.

7

X

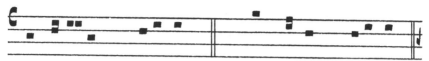

KY-RI-e *e - LE-I-SON.IIJ. CHRI-STE e - LE-I-SON.IIJ.
LORD, have mer-cy.   CHRIST, have mer-cy.

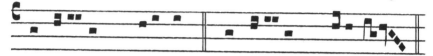

KY-RI-e e - LE-I-SON.IJ. KY-RI-e e - LE-I-SON.
LORD, have mer-cy.   LORD, have mer-cy.

XI
DEUS GENITOR ALME

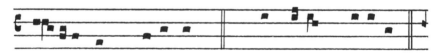

KY-RI-e *e - LE-I-SON.IIJ. CHRI-STE e - LE-I-SON.IIJ.
LORD, have mer-cy.   CHRIST, have mer-cy.

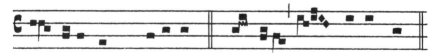

KY-RI-e e - LE-I-SON.IJ. KY-RI-e e - LE-I-SON.
LORD, have mer-cy.   LORD, have mer- cy.

XII
DE ANGELIS

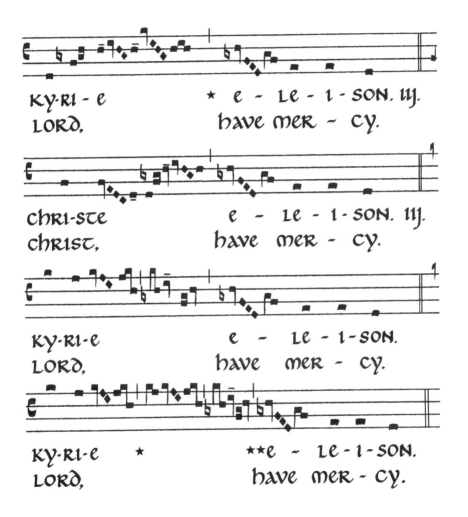

KY·RI - e   ★ e - Le - ι - SON. iιj.
LORD,   have meR - cy.

chRI-STe   e - Le - ι - SON. iιj.
chRIST,   have meR - cy.

KY·RI-e   e - Le - ι - SON.
LORD,   have meR - cy.

KY·RI-e   ★   ★★e - Le - ι - SON.
LORD,   have meR - cy.

9

KY-RI-e ★   e - LE-I-SON. KY-RI-e   e -
LORD,   have mer-cy.   LORD,   have

LE-I-SON. KY-RI-e   e - LE-I-SON. CHRI-STE
MER-cy. LORD,   have mer-cy. CHRIST,

e - LE-I-SON. CHRI - STE   e - LE-I-SON.
have mer-cy. CHRIST,   have mer-cy.

CHRI-STE   e - LE-I-SON. KY-RI-e
CHRIST,   have mer-cy. LORD,

e - LE-I-SON. KY-RI-e   e - LE-I-SON. KY-RI-
have mer-cy. LORD,   have mer-cy. LORD,

-e ★ ★★ e - LE-I-SON.
have mer-cy.

XIV
ALME PATER

KY-RI- e★e - LE-I-SON. KY-RI- e e - LE-I-SON.
LORD, have mer-cy. LORD, have mer-cy.

KY-RI- e e - LE-I-SON. CHRI-STE e - LE-I-SON.
LORD, have mer-cy. christ, have mer-cy.

CHRI-STE e - LE-I-SON. CHRI-STE e - LE-I-SON.
CHRIST, have mer-cy christ have mer-cy.

KY-RI-e e - LE-I-SON. KY-RI-e e - LE-I-SON.
LORD, have mer-cy. LORD, have mer-cy.

11

KY-RI-E   ★   ★★   e – LE-I-SON.
LORD,   have mer-cy.

XV
TE CHRISTE REX SUPPLICES

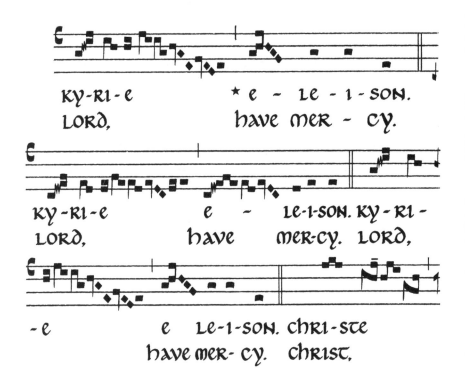

KY-RI-E   ★ e – LE – I – SON.
LORD,   have mer – cy.

KY-RI-E   e – LE-I-SON. KY – RI –
LORD,   have   mer-cy. LORD,

-e   e LE-I-SON. CHRI-STE
have mer- cy.   CHRIST,

e - LE-1-SON. CHRI-STE e - LE-1-SON.
have mer-cy. christ have mer-cy.

chRI-STE e - LE-1-SON. KY-RI - e
christ, have mer-cy. LORD,

e - LE-1-SON. KY-RI - e e - LE-1-SON. KY - RI-
have mer-cy. LORD, have mer-cy. LORD,

-e ★ ★★ e - LE-1-SON.
         have mer-cy.

GLORIA

1

GLO-RY TO GOD IN THE HIGH-EST,* AND

PEACE TO HIS PEO-PLE ON EARTH. LORD GOD,

HEAVEN-LY KING, AL-MIGHT-Y GOD AND FA-

-THER, WE WOR-SHIP YOU, WE GIVE YOU

THANKS, WE PRAISE YOU FOR YOUR GLO-RY.

LORD JE-SUS CHRIST, ON-LY SON OF THE FA-THER,

LORD GOD, LAMB OF GOD, YOU TAKE A-WAY

THE SIN OF THE WORLD: HAVE MER-CY ON US;

YOU ARE SEAT-ED AT THE RIGHT HAND OF THE

FA-THER: RE-CEIVE OUR PRAYER. FOR YOU

A-LONE ARE THE HO-LY ONE, YOU A-LONE

ARE THE LORD, YOU A-LONE ARE THE MOST

HIGH, JE - SUS CHRIST, WITH THE HO-LY

SPI-RIT, IN THE GLO-RY OF GOD THE FA - THER.

A - MEN.

11

GLO-RY TO GOD IN THE HIGH-EST, AND PEACE

TO HIS PEO-PLE ON EARTH. LORD GOD, HEAVEN-

-LY KING, AL-MIGHT-Y GOD AND FA-THER,

WE WOR-SHIP YOU, WE GIVE YOU THANKS,

WE PRAISE YOU FOR YOUR GLO-RY. LORD

JE-SUS CHRIST, ON-LY SON OF THE FA-THER,

LORD GOD, LAMB OF GOD, YOU TAKE A-

WAY THE SIN OF THE WORLD: HAVE MER-CY

ON US; YOU ARE SEAT-ED AT THE RIGHT

HAND OF THE FA-THER: RE-CEIVE OUR

PRAYER. FOR YOU A-LONE ARE THE HO-LY

ONE, YOU A-LONE ARE THE LORD, YOU A-

LONE ARE THE MOST HIGH, JE - SUS CHRIST,

WITH THE HO-LY SPI-RIT, IN THE GLO-RY

OF GOD THE FA - THER. A - MEN.

III

GLO - RY TO GOD IN THE HIGH-EST, * AND

PEACE TO HIS PEO-PLE ON EARTH. LORD

GOD, HEAVEN-LY KING, AL-MIGHT-Y GOD

AND FA-THER, WE WOR-SHIP YOU, WE

GIVE YOU THANKS, WE PRAISE YOU FOR

YOUR GLO-RY. LORD JE-SUS CHRIST, ON-LY

SON OF THE FA-THER, LORD GOD, LAMB OF

GOD, YOU TAKE A-WAY THE SIN OF THE WORLD:

HAVE MER-CY ON US; YOU ARE SEAT-ED AT

THE RIGHT HAND OF THE FA-THER: RE-CEIVE

OUR PRAYER. FOR YOU A-LONE ARE THE

ho-ly one, you a-lone are the LORD, you

a-lone are the most high, Je-sus Christ,

with the ho-ly spi - rit, in the glo-ry

of god the fa-ther. a – men.

IV

GLO -RY to god in the high-est, * and

peace to his peo-ple on earth. LORD

GOD, HEAVEN-LY KING, AL - MIGHT - Y GOD

AND FA-THER, WE WOR-SHIP YOU, WE GIVE

YOU THANKS, WE PRAISE YOU FOR YOUR

GLO-RY. LORD JE-SUS CHRIST, ON-LY SON

OF THE FA - THER, LORD GOD, LAMB OF GOD,

YOU TAKE A-WAY THE SIN OF THE WORLD:

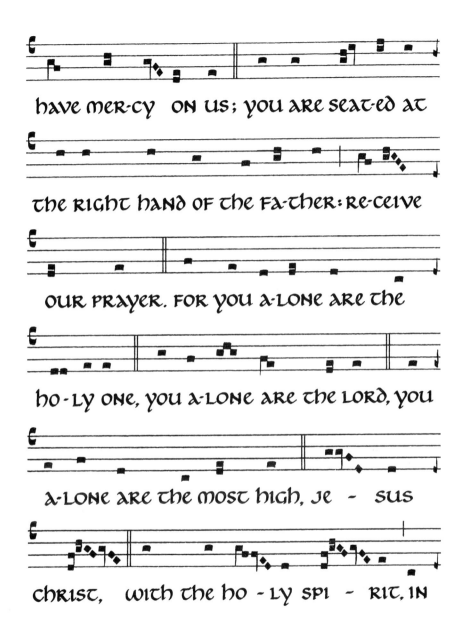

have mer-cy on us; you are seat-ed at

the right hand of the Fa-ther: Re-ceive

our prayer. For you a-lone are the

ho-ly one, you a-lone are the Lord, you

a-lone are the most high, Je - sus

christ, with the ho - ly spi - Rit, in

THE GLO-RY OF GOD THE FA -THER. A - MEN.

V

GLO-RY TO GOD IN THE HIGH-EST, AND PEACE

TO HIS PEO-PLE ON EARTH. LORD GOD, HEAVEN-

-LY KING, AL-MIGHT-Y GOD AND FA-THER,

WE WOR-SHIP YOU, WE GIVE YOU THANKS, WE

PRAISE YOU FOR YOUR GLO-RY. LORD JE -

-sus christ, on-ly son of the fa-ther, lord

god, lamb of god, you take a-way the

sin of the world: have mer - cy on us;

you are seat-ed at the right hand of the

fa-ther: re - ceive our prayer. for you

a-lone are the ho-ly one, you a-lone

ARE THE LORD, YOU A-LONE ARE THE MOST HIGH,

JE-SUS CHRIST, WITH THE HO-LY SPI-RIT, IN THE

GLO-RY OF GOD THE FA-THER. A ~ MEN.

VI

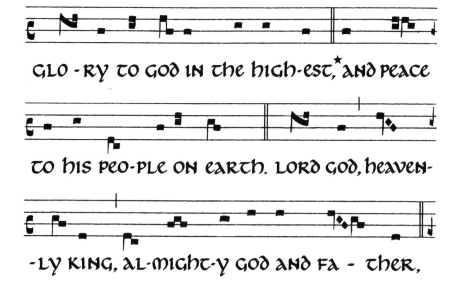

GLO - RY TO GOD IN THE HIGH-EST, AND PEACE

TO HIS PEO-PLE ON EARTH. LORD GOD, HEAVEN-

-LY KING, AL-MIGHT-Y GOD AND FA - THER,

we wor-ship you, we give you thanks, we praise you for your glo-ry. Lord Je-sus Christ, on-ly Son of the Fa - ther, Lord God, Lamb of God, you take a-way the sin of the world: have mer-cy on us; you are seat-ed at the right hand of

the FA-THER: RE-CEIVE OUR PRAYER. FOR you

a-LONE ARE THE HO-LY ONE, you a-LONE

ARE THE LORD, you a-LONE ARE THE MOST

HIGH, JE-SUS CHRIST, WITH THE HO - LY

SPI - RIT, IN THE GLO-RY OF GOD THE FA-THER.

a - MEN.

GLO-RY TO GOD IN THE HIGH-EST,* AND PEACE

TO HIS PEO-PLE ON EARTH. LORD GOD, HEA-VEN

-LY KING, AL-MIGHT-Y GOD AND FA-THER, WE

WOR-SHIP YOU, WE GIVE YOU THANKS, WE

PRAISE YOU FOR YOUR GLO-RY. LORD JE-SUS

CHRIST, ON-LY SON OF THE FA-THER, LORD

GOD, LAMB OF GOD, YOU TAKE A WAY THE

SIN OF THE WORLD: HAVE MER-CY ON US;

YOU ARE SEAT-ED AT THE RIGHT HAND OF

THE FA-THER: RE-CEIVE OUR PRAYER. FOR

YOU A-LONE ARE THE HO-LY ONE, YOU A-

-LONE ARE THE LORD, YOU A-LONE ARE THE

most high, Jesus Christ, with the holy SPI-RIT,

IN the GLO-RY OF GOD the FA - ther. A - MEN.

VIII

GLO-RY to GOD IN the high-est,* and peace

to his peo-ple ON earth.   LORD GOD,

heaven-ly KING, AL-might-y GOD and

FA-ther, we wor-ship you, we give   you

thanks, we praise you for your glo-ry.

lord je-sus christ, on-ly son of the fa-

-ther, lord god, lamb of god, you take

a-way the sin of the world: have mer-

-cy on us; you are seat-ed at the right

hand of the fa-ther: re-ceive   our

PRAYER. FOR YOU A-LONE ARE THE HO-LY ONE,

YOU A-LONE ARE THE LORD, YOU A-LONE ARE

THE MOST HIGH, JE-SUS CHRIST, WITH THE HO-

-LY SPI-RIT, IN THE GLO-RY OF GOD THE FA-THER.

A - MEN.

IX

GLO- RY TO GOD IN THE HIGH-EST, * AND

peace to his peo-ple on earth. Lord

god, heaven-ly king, al-might-y god

and fa-ther, we wor-ship you, we

give you thanks, we praise you for

your glo-ry. Lord Je-sus Christ, on-ly

son of the fa-ther, Lord god, Lamb of

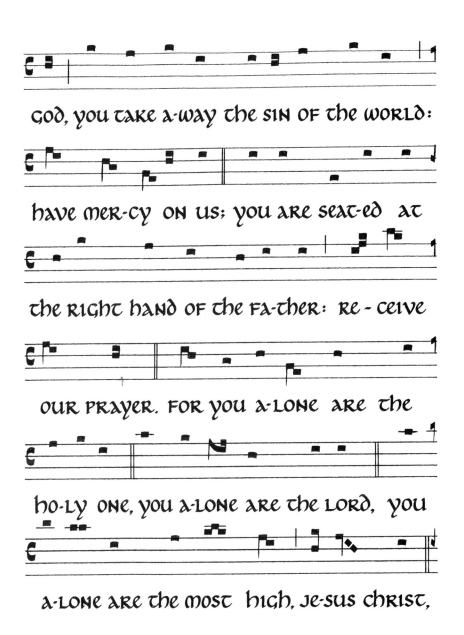

God, you take a-way the sin of the world:

have mer-cy on us; you are seat-ed at

the right hand of the Fa-ther: re - ceive

our prayer. For you a-lone are the

ho-ly one, you a-lone are the Lord, you

a-lone are the most high, Je-sus Christ,

with the ho-ly spi-rit, in the glo-ry
of god the fa-ther. a ~ men.

x

glo-ry to god in the high-est, * and
peace to his peo-ple on earth. lord
god, heaven-ly king, al-might-y god
and fa-ther, we wor-ship you, we

GIVE YOU THANKS, WE PRAISE YOU FOR YOUR

GLO-RY. LORD JE-SUS CHRIST, ON-LY SON OF

THE FA-THER, LORD GOD, LAMB OF GOD, YOU

TAKE A-WAY THE SIN OF THE WORLD: HAVE

MER-CY ON US; YOU ARE SEAT-ED AT THE

RIGHT HAND OF THE FA-THER: RE-CEIVE OUR

PRAYER. FOR YOU A-LONE ARE THE HO-LY

ONE, YOU A-LONE ARE THE LORD, YOU A-

LONE ARE THE MOST HIGH, JE-SUS CHRIST,

WITH THE HO - LY SPI - RIT, IN THE GLO-

-RY OF GOD THE FA - THER. A - MEN.

XI

GLO-RY TO GOD IN THE HIGH-EST, * AND

38

peace to his peo-ple on earth. lord

god, hea-ven-ly king, al-might-y god

and fa-ther, we wor-ship you, we give

you thanks, we praise you for

your glo-ry. lord je-sus christ, on-ly

son of the fa-ther, lord god, lamb of

GOD, you take a-way the SIN OF the

WORLD: have mer-cy on us; you are

seat-ed at the right hand of the FA-

-ther: re-ceive our prayer. FOR you a-

-lone are the ho-ly one, you a-lone

are the LORD, you a-lone are the MOST

hich, Je-sus christ,   with the ho-ly

SPI-RIT, IN the GLO-Ry OF GOD the FA-ther.

a - MEN.

CREDO

1

We be-lieve in one God, the Fa-ther, the al-might-y, mak-er of hea-ven and earth, of all that is, seen and un-seen.

We be-lieve in one Lord, Je-sus Christ, the on-ly Son of God, e-ter-nal-ly Be-got

-ten of the Fa-ther, God from God,

Light from light, true God from true

God, be-got-ten not made, of one be-ing

with the Fa-ther. through him all

1.

things were made. For us men and for

Our Sal-va-tion he came down from

1. For revised text see page 76.

hea-ven: by the power of the ho-ly spi -

-rit he be-came in-car-nate from the
[OF]

vir-gin mary, and was made man. for

our sake he was cru-ci-fied un - der pon-

-tius pi-late; he suf-fered death and

was bur-ied. on the third day he rose

44

a-gain in ac-cord-ance with the scrip -

-tures; he a-scend-ed in-to hea-ven and

is seat-ed at the right hand of the fa-

-ther. he will come a-gain in glo-ry to

judge the liv-ing and the dead, and his

king-dom will have no end. we be-lieve

IN the ho-ly spi-rit, the Lord, the giv-

-er of life, who pro-ceeds from the fa-

-ther and the son. with the fa-ther and

the son he is wor-shipped and glo-ri-

-fied. he has spo-ken through the pro-

-phets. we be-lieve in one ho-ly cath-o-

-LIC AND A-PO-STO-LIC church. we ac-

-KNOW-LEDGE ONE BAP-TISM FOR the FOR-

-GIVE-NESS OF SINS. we LOOK FOR the RE -

-SUR-REC-TION OF the dead, and the LIFE

OF the world to come. a - men.

11

we be-lieve in one god, the fa-ther, the

AL-MIGHT-Y, MAK-ER OF HEA-VEN AND EARTH,

OF ALL THAT IS, SEEN AND UN-SEEN. WE

BE-LIEVE IN ONE LORD, JE-SUS CHRIST, THE

ON-LY SON OF GOD, E-TER-NAL-LY BE-GOT-

-TEN OF THE FA-THER, GOD FROM GOD,

LIGHT FROM LIGHT, TRUE GOD FROM

TRUE GOD, BE-GOT-TEN NOT MADE, OF ONE BE-

-ING WITH THE FA-THER. THROUGH HIM ALL

1.

THINGS WERE MADE. FOR US MEN AND FOR

OUR SAL-VA-TION HE CAME DOWN FROM

HEA-VEN: BY THE POWER OF THE HO-LY SPI-

-RIT HE BE-CAME IN-CAR-NATE FROM THE

[OF]

1. For revised text see page 76.

★ FOR US

VIR-GIN MA-RY, AND WAS MADE MAN. FOR

OUR SAKE he WAS CRU-CI-FIED UN-DER

PON-TIUS PI-LATE; he SUF-FERED death

AND WAS BUR-IED. ON the third day

he ROSE A-GAIN IN AC-CORD-ANCE WITH

the SCRIP-TURES; he A-SCEND-ED IN-TO

hea-ven and is seat-ed at the right

hand of the fa-ther. he will come

a-gain in glo-ry to judge the liv-

-ing and the dead, and his king-dom

will have no end. we be-lieve in the

ho-ly spi-rit, the lord, the giv-er of

LIFE, WHO PRO-CEEDS FROM THE FA-THER

AND THE SON. WITH THE FA-THER AND

THE SON HE IS WOR-SHIPPED AND GLO-RI-

-FIED. HE HAS SPO-KEN THROUGH THE

PRO-PHETS. WE BE-LIEVE IN ONE HO-LY

CATH-O-LIC AND A-PO-STO-LIC CHURCH.

WE AC-KNOW-LEDGE ONE BAP-TISM FOR

the FOR-GIVE-NESS OF SINS. WE LOOK FOR

the RE-SUR-REC-TION OF the dead, and

the LIFE OF the WORLD to come.

A - MEN.

SANCTUS

1

Ho - ly, * ho - ly, ho - ly Lord, God of power and might, hea-ven and earth are full of your glo-ry. Ho-san-na in the high- -est. Bless-ed is he who comes in the

NAME OF the LORD. HO-SAN-NA IN

the high-est.

11

ho - ly,* ho-ly, ho - ly LORD,

GOD OF POWER AND MIGHT, hea-ven

AND earth are FULL OF YOUR GLO-RY.

ho-san-na in the high - est. BLESS-ed is

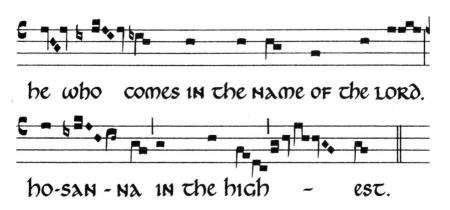

he who comes in the name of the lord.

ho-san-na in the high - est.

III

ho - ly,* ho-ly, ho - ly lord,

god of power and might, heav'n and

earth are full of your glo-ry. ho-

san-na in the high - est. bless-ed

56

is he who comes in the name of the lord.

ho - san-na in the high - est.

IV

ho-ly,* ho - ly, ho-ly lord, god of power

and might, hea-ven and earth are full

of your glo-ry. ho-san-na in

the high-est. bless-ed is he who comes in

the name of the lord. ho-san-na

in the high-est.

v

ho - ly,* ho - ly, ho - ly lord, god of

power and might, hea-ven and earth

are full of your glo -ry. ho - san-

-na in the high-est. bless-ed is he

who comes ɪɴ ᴛʜe ɴᴀᴍe ᴏꜰ ᴛʜe ʟᴏʀᴅ. ho -

- ꜱᴀɴ - ɴᴀ   ɪɴ ᴛʜe high - eꜱᴛ.

VI

ho - ʟʏ, * ho - ʟʏ, ho-ʟʏ ʟᴏʀᴅ, ɢᴏᴅ ᴏꜰ

ᴘᴏwᴇʀ ᴀɴᴅ ᴍɪɢʜᴛ, hea-ᴠᴇɴ ᴀɴᴅ ᴇᴀʀᴛh

ᴀʀᴇ ꜰᴜʟʟ ᴏꜰ ʏᴏᴜʀ ɢʟᴏ-ʀʏ. ho-ꜱᴀɴ-ɴᴀ

ɪɴ ᴛʜe high - eꜱᴛ. ʙʟᴇꜱꜱ-ᴇᴅ ɪꜱ he who

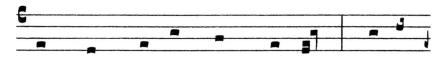

comes in the name of the lord. ho-san-

-na in the high - est.

vii

ho - ly, *ho - ly, ho-ly lord, god of

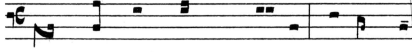

power and might, hea-ven and earth

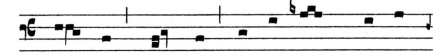

are full of your glo-ry. ho-san-na

in the high-est. bless-ed is he who

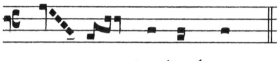

comes in the name of the lord. ho-san-

-na in the high-est.

viii

ho-ly,* ho-ly, ho-ly lord, god of

power and might, hea-ven and earth

are full of your glo-ry. ho-san-

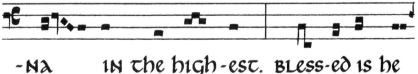

-na in the high-est. bless-ed is he

who comes in the name of the lord. ho -

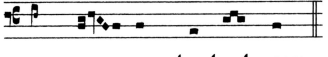

san-na in the high-est.

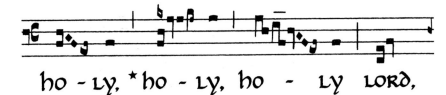

ho - ly, *ho - ly, ho - ly lord,

god of power and might, hea-ven and

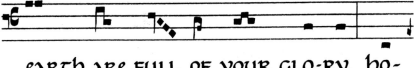

earth are full of your glo-ry. ho-

san-na in the high - est. bless-ed is

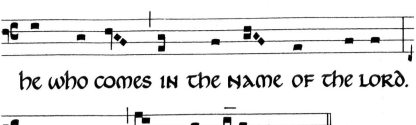

he who comes in the name of the lord.

ho-san-na in the high - est.

x

ho-ly, * ho-ly, ho-ly lord, god of

power and might, hea-ven and earth

are full of your glo-ry. ho-san-na

in the high-est. bless-ed is he who comes

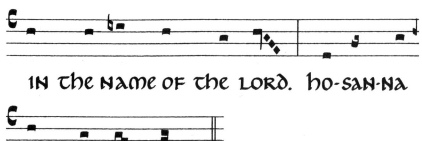

IN the name of the lord. ho-san-na

IN the high-est.

XI

ho-ly, *ho-ly, ho-ly lord, god of

power and might, hea-ven and earth

are full of your glo-ry. ho-san-na

IN the high-est. bless-ed is he who

comes in the name of the lord. ho-san-

-na in the high - est.

AGNUS

1

L amb of god, ★ you take a-way the

sins of the world: have mer - cy on us.

lamb of god, ★ you take a-way the sins

of the world: have mer - cy on us. lamb

of god, ★ you take a-way the sins of

the world : grant us peace.

Lamb of God, * you take a-way the sins

of the world: have mer-cy on us.

Lamb of God, * you take a-way the sins

of the world: have mer-cy on us. Lamb

of God, * you take a-way the sins of

the world: GRANT US PEACE.

III

LAMB OF GOD, * you take a-way the sins

OF the world: have mer-cy on us. LAMB

OF GOD, * you take a-way the sins OF

the world: have mer-cy on us. LAMB

OF GOD, * you take a-way the sins OF

the WORLD: GRANT US PEACE.

IV

LAMB OF GOD,*you take   a-way the

sins of the world: have mer-cy on us.ij.

LAMB OF GOD,*you take   a-way the

sins of the world: grant   us peace.

V

LAMB OF GOD, * you take a-way the sins

of the world: have mer - cy on us. ij.

LAMB OF GOD, *you take a-way the sins

of the world: GRANT us peace.

VI

LAMB OF GOD,* you take a-way the sins

of the world: have mer-cy on us. ij.

LAMB OF GOD, * you take a-way the

SINS OF the WORLD : GRANT US PEACE.

VII

LAMB OF GOD, * you take a-way the SINS

OF the WORLD: have MER - CY ON US.

LAMB OF GOD, * you take a-way the SINS

OF the WORLD: have MER - CY ON US.

71

LAMB OF GOD,*you take a-way the sins of the world: GRANT us peace.

VIII

LAMB OF GOD, *you take a-way the sins of the world: have mer-cy on us.

LAMB OF GOD, * you take a -way the sins of the world: have mer-cy on us.

LAMB OF GOD, * you take a-way the sins

OF the WORLD: GRANT US PEACE.

IX

LAMB OF GOD, * you take a-way the sins

OF the WORLD: have mer -cy ON us. ij.

LAMB OF GOD, * you take a-way the sins

OF the WORLD: GRANT US PEACE.

LAMB OF GOD, * you take a-way the sins

OF the WORLD: have mer-cy on us. ij.

LAMB OF GOD, * you take away the sins

OF the WORLD: GRANT US PEACE.

xi

LAMB OF GOD, * you take a-way the

SINS OF the WORLD: have mer-cy on us. ij.

LAMB OF GOD,* you take a-way the

SINS OF the WORLD: GRANT US PEACE.

✗ [ALTERNATIVE WORDING]

JE-SUS,* LAMB OF GOD: have mer-cy on

us. JE-SUS,* BEAR-ER OF OUR SINS: have

mer-cy on us. JE-SUS,* RE-DEEM-ER OF

the WORLD: GIVE US YOUR PEACE.

CREDO

1

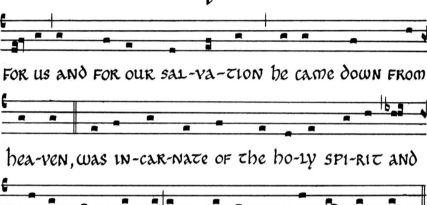

FOR US AND FOR OUR SAL-VA-TION he came down from

hea-ven, was in-car-nate of the ho-ly spi-rit and

the VIR-GIN MA-RY and Be-came TRU-LY hu-man.

11

FOR US AND FOR OUR SAL-VA-TION he came down from

hea-ven, was in-car-nate of the ho-ly spi-rit and

the VIR-GIN MA-RY and Be-came TRU-LY hu-man.

TABLE OF MODELS

KYRIE ELEISON

I	'Lux et origo'	Salisbury XIII	(P M M S V)
II	'Rex splendens'	Salisbury XIV	(P M M S IV)
III	'Cunctipotens'	Salisbury XV	(P M M S VIII)
IV	'Orbis factor'	Salisbury XVI	(P M M S VII)
V		Salisbury XX	(P M M S XVI)
VI		Salisbury XXIII	(P M M S IX)
VII	'Dominator Deus'	Salisbury XXI	(P M M S XVII)
VIII		Salisbury XXIV	(P M M S X)
IX	'Fons bonitatis'	Vatican II	(Salisbury III with tropes, P M M S III)
X		Vatican XVI	(P M M S XIX)
XI	'Deus genitor'	Vatican XVIII	
XII	'De angelis'	Vatican VIII	
XIII	'Cum iubilo'	Vatican IX	
XIV	'Alme Pater'	Vatican X	
XV	'Te Christe rex'	Vatican ad lib. VI (= IA in 1974 *Graduale*)	

GLORIA

I	Salisbury I	(Vatican III, P M M S I)
II	Salisbury II	(Vatican XI, P M M S II)
III	Salisbury III	(Vatican X, P M M S III)
IV	Salisbury IV	(Vatican IV, P M M S IV)
V	Salisbury V	(Vatican V, P M M S IX)
VI	Salisbury VI	(Vatican VII, P M M S V)
VII	Vatican XV	(Salisbury VII, P M M S VI)
VIII	Salisbury VIII	(Vatican XIV, P M M S VII)
IX	Vatican IX	(Salisbury IX with tropes, P M M S VIII)
X	Vatican VIII	
XI	Vatican ad lib. IV	(Ambrosian)

CREDO

I	Salisbury	(Vatican I, P M M S)
II	Vatican III	

SANCTUS

I	Salisbury I	(Vatican II, P M M S I)
II	Salisbury II	(Vatican VIII, P M M S II)
III	Salisbury III	(Vatican IV, P M M S III)
IV	Salisbury IV	(Vatican IX, P M M S IV)
V	Salisbury V	(Vatican XVII, P M M S V)
VI	Salisbury VI	(Vatican XIII, P M M S VI)
VII	Salisbury VII	(P M M S VII)
VIII	Salisbury VIII	(Vatican XV, P M M S IX)
IX	Salisbury IX	(Vatican XII, P M M S VIII)
X	Salisbury X	(Vatican XVIII, P M M S X)
XI	Vatican ad lib. I	

AGNUS

I	Salisbury I	(Vatican XII, P M M S I)
II	Salisbury II	(Vatican IV, P M M S II)
III	Salisbury III	(Vatican XIV, P M M S III)
IV	Salisbury IV	(Vatican VI, P M M S IV)
V	Salisbury V	(Vatican I, P M M S VII)
VI	Salisbury VI	(Vatican II, P M M S V)
VII	Salisbury VII	(Vatican VIII, P M M S VI)
VIII	Salisbury VIII	(P M M S VIII)
IX	Salisbury IX	(Vatican XV, P M M S IX)
X	Salisbury X	(Vatican XVIII, P M M S X)
XI	Vatican ad lib. II	